Teddy Bear Treasury

By Maureen Spurgeon

Brown Watson

ENGLAND

Contents

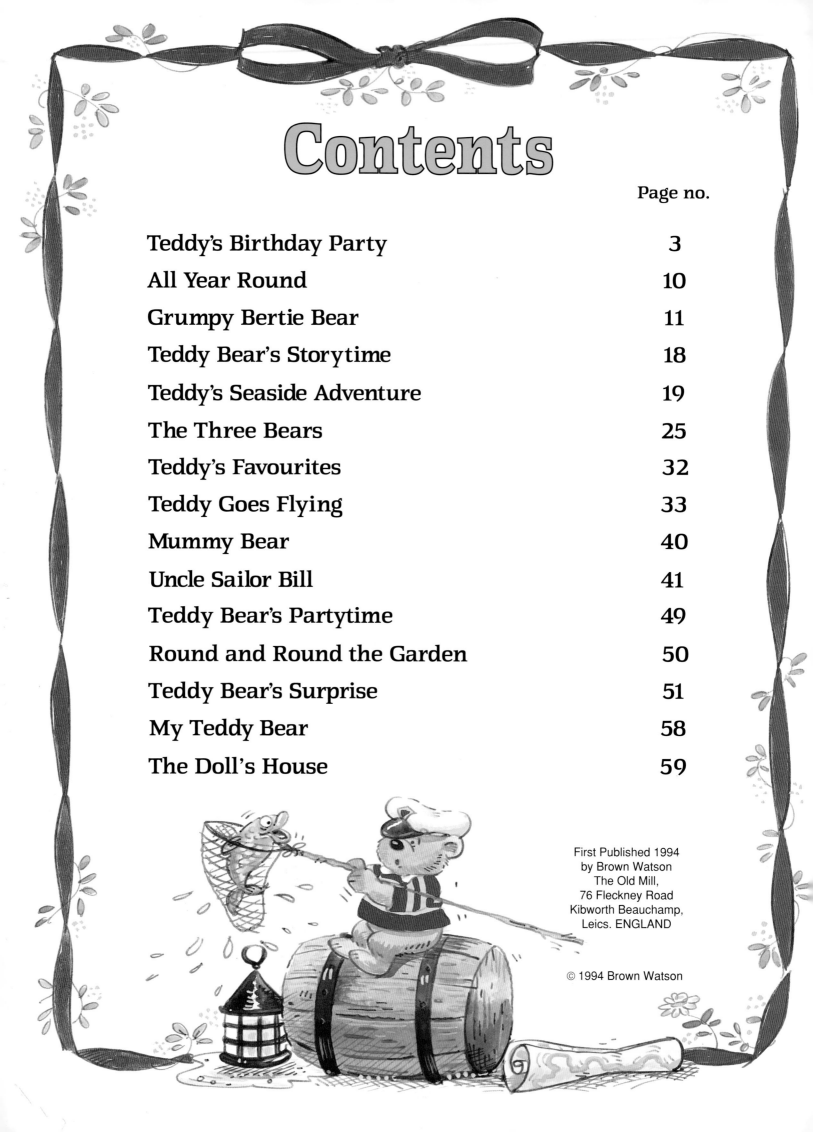

First Published 1994
by Brown Watson
The Old Mill,
76 Fleckney Road
Kibworth Beauchamp,
Leics. ENGLAND

Teddy's Birthday Party

It was the day of Aunt Bertha Bear's birthday,
and everyone was very busy getting
things ready for a special birthday party.
There were cakes and jellies,
ice creams, sweets, pies, rolls, crisps
and banana boats . . . no wonder Teddy Bear
and his friends could hardly wait for the
fun to begin!

"We'll play lots of jolly games," Aunt Bertha Bear told everyone. "Then Grandfather Bear has promised to bring his Punch and Judy show along!"

That made Teddy Bear smile around at his friends. If there was one thing they enjoyed as much as a birthday party, it was a Punch and Judy Show!

They were halfway through a game of
Musical Chairs before Grandpa Bear
arrived. And he did not seem in a party
mood at all.
"Just look what's happened to poor old
Mr. Punch!" he said, showing them all.
"I got his nose caught in the travelling case,
and I can't possibly mend him in time!"

There was a chorus of disappointed sighs.
"Oh, dear!" said Mummy Bear. "And I suppose Marmaduke is still with Great Uncle Bertram Bear?"
"Yes, indeed," murmured Grandpa. "Ah, my good friend, Marmaduke! If only he were here, now . . ."
"Marmaduke?" echoed Teddy Bear. "Who's Marmaduke?"

"Marmaduke . . ."
Mummy Bear sighed again.
"How he used to make everyone laugh . . ."
"Who's Marmaduke?" Teddy wanted to know. "Always a great favourite . . ." added Grandpa Bear.
"But – who IS Marmaduke?" Teddy asked again, in a much louder voice this time.

7

Grandpa Bear looked at Mummy Bear. She looked at Grandpa. They both looked at Teddy. "Marmaduke?" said Mummy Bear at last. "Everyone likes Marmaduke!" "And I'm sure, Teddy Bear," smiled Grandpa, "that you and your friends will like him, too!" Teddy was very puzzled. Hadn't Mummy said Marmaduke was visiting Great Uncle Bertram?

"Where's Teddy?" asked Barney, as they played Pass the Parcel. "He's missing all the party games!" Before anyone could answer, Mummy Bear clapped her hands. "Please take your seats," she said, "for the birthday show, presented by Grandpa Bear – and Marmaduke!"

"Marmaduke . . ." the whisper went around the room. "Who's Marmaduke?" Aunt Bertha Bear drew the curtains – and who do you think it was? That's right! Teddy Bear, sitting on Grandpa's knee and pretending to be Marmaduke, his dummy!

How the bears laughed at the silly things they did and the funny things Teddy said in the squeaky voice which was really Grandpa's!

9

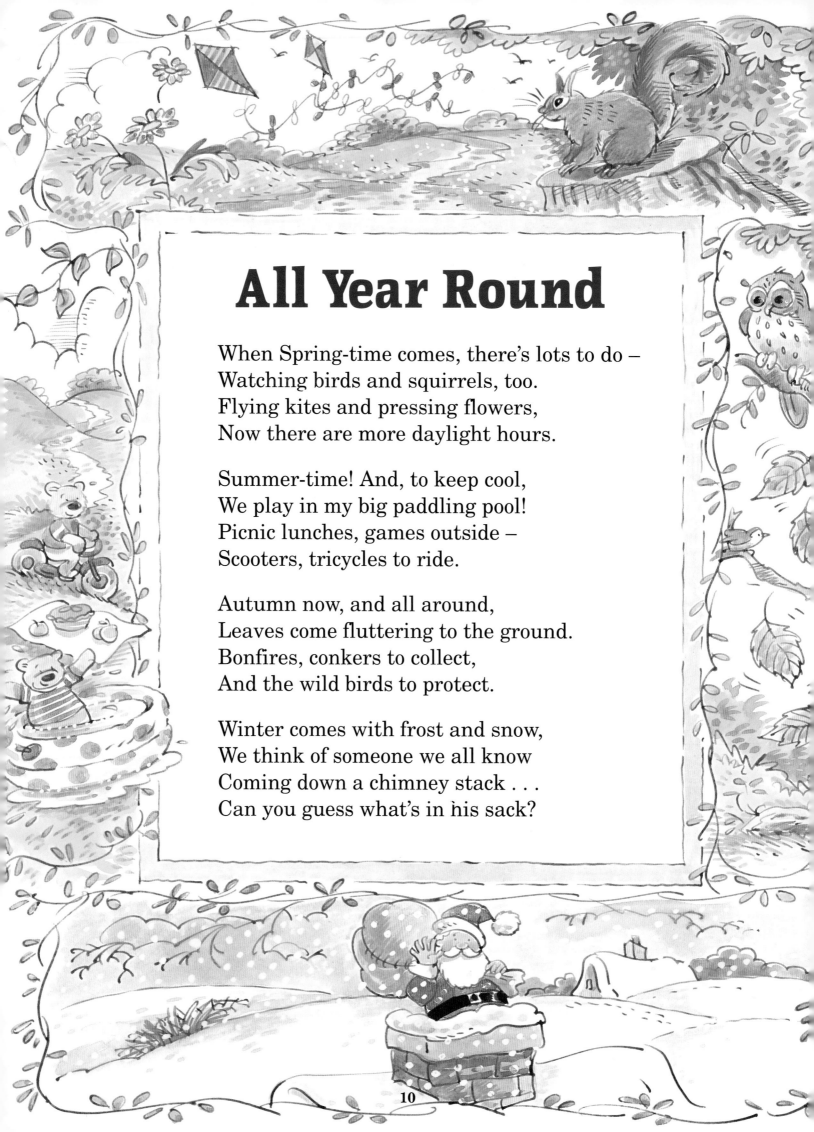

All Year Round

When Spring-time comes, there's lots to do –
Watching birds and squirrels, too.
Flying kites and pressing flowers,
Now there are more daylight hours.

Summer-time! And, to keep cool,
We play in my big paddling pool!
Picnic lunches, games outside –
Scooters, tricycles to ride.

Autumn now, and all around,
Leaves come fluttering to the ground.
Bonfires, conkers to collect,
And the wild birds to protect.

Winter comes with frost and snow,
We think of someone we all know
Coming down a chimney stack . . .
Can you guess what's in his sack?

Grumpy Bertie Bear

Near the cottage where Teddy Bear lives with his Mummy and Daddy there are some lovely woods. He and Daddy Bear often go out walking and love to see all the birds and woodland friends.

"We've had a lot of rain lately," said Daddy one morning. "The ground's too wet to go far, Teddy, so I think . . ."

Teddy grabbed his Daddy's arm. "Listen!" he said. "I'm sure I heard a voice!"

"ATISHOO!" someone sneezed. "Oh, dear! Oh, dear! I feel so dreadful! And I ache all over!"

"Sounds like another bear!" cried Daddy, leading the way through the trees.

"Look, just under this clump of bushes."

"Who are you?" asked Teddy Bear kindly.

"The name's Bertie," answered the bear, sneezing again. "Ooh, I'm soaked to the skin!"

"You'd best come home with us," said Daddy Bear. "Take his arm, Teddy."

Before long, Bertie was sitting in Daddy's chair with Teddy's dressing gown on. And as he sipped a nice cup of hot chocolate, he began telling his story.

"I belong to a girl called Lavinia," he said.

He looked all around the cosy, little cottage.

"The house where we live is much bigger than this!" he added. Mummy Bear bit her lip.

"So, how did you come to be left in the woods?" asked Teddy politely.

"Lavinia went off picking flowers," growled Bertie. "I suppose she got caught in the rain and ran straight home. She would never have left me behind on purpose."

13

"No, of course not," smiled Daddy. "Look, we'll find you some dry clothes, then go back to the woods when you're feeling better, Bertie. Maybe Lavinia will be there looking for you."

Teddy managed to find a pair of trousers and a warm, woolly jumper to fit Bertie – even a pair of smart shoes and socks!

"Try these on for size, Bertie," he smiled.

Bertie Bear did not seem very pleased.

"Not really my colour," he said, fingering the jersey. "And Lavinia threw out a pair of trousers much better than these!" He gave a deep sigh. "Still, I suppose they are better than nothing. I'll get a whole set of new clothes once I'm back home, anyway."

"What a nasty, old bear," thought Teddy. "He hasn't even said "Thank You", yet!"

15

In the end, Mummy, Daddy and Teddy Bear were glad when the time came for Bertie to go back to the woods. Daddy and Teddy waited to see if the little girl would come back to find him. Presently, they heard a voice.

"Lavinia, dear, come here a minute!"

It was a little, old lady, squeezing her way towards the clump of bushes where Bertie sat.

"Lavinia," she smiled, as a little girl appeared, "isn't this the bear you lost the other day?" It was then that Teddy saw the lovely doll which Lavinia held.

"What, that old thing, Auntie?" she cried "Look at him. Somebody must have thrown him away!"

16

Bertie looked as if he were about to cry. She went off, leaving the old lady to pick up Bertie Bear.

"Do you know," she said, stroking his head, "you remind me of a Teddy Bear I had when I was a girl, about the same age as my great niece, Lavinia. How would you like to come home with me? I'm sure my grandchildren would love to play with you when they come to tea."

The hurt look on Bertie Bear's face vanished in an instant.

Teddy could see the corners of his mouth turning up into a happy smile, his black eyes shining like new, just to know that he was loved and wanted once again.

"What are you thinking about, Teddy?" asked Daddy.

"I was just wondering," said Teddy, "if Bertie Bear will call at our cottage again."

17

Teddy Bear's Storytime

Teddy Bear got into a bit of a muddle when he tried telling this story to Teacher Bear! See if you can help, by pointing to the pictures in the right order!

1

2

3

4

5

6

7

8

9

Answer:- 5,7,2,4,8,1,3,6,9

Teddy's Seaside Adventure

Teddy Bear was enjoying himself at the seaside!
There was so much to do! Best of all,
there was a beach competition, with prizes
for the best sand-castles. The competition was
being judged by Captain Bear – and everyone
was wondering who would win! Captain Bear
had been showing Teddy and his friends how
to build the very best sand-castles –

so, even without any prizes, they'd
already had lots of fun! The only snag
was Bully Bear . . . He was forever
teasing the little bears, spoiling their
sand-castles, running off with their
sweets and burying things in the sand.

"I'd like to give that bear a few things!" growled Captain Bear. "Like a good spanking and no sweets for a fortnight!" "Bully's too strong for any of us!" said Barney Bear, Teddy's friend. "What can we do, Teddy?"

Teddy Bear did not answer. It was very hard to think of a way to beat a big bear like Bully. Later on, Teddy gave Teeny Bear an envelope. "Can you take this to Teacher Bear, Teeny?" he said. "Captain Bear's written down where all the prizes for the sand-castle competition have been hidden, so that Bully Bear doesn't find them!"

"That's what you think, Teddy Bear!" said Bully Bear.
He snatched the letter and ran off, laughing.
All that afternoon, Teddy and his friends worked hard
on their sand-castles. "Well," said Barney, "at least
you got Bully Bear out of the way, Teddy!" He did not
say anything about them losing all the prizes for the
sand-castle competition – but the bears could not help
being disappointed . . .

Suddenly, Captain Bear gave an angry yell. "What do you mean by digging up my sandcastle?" he roared at Bully Bear. "You ruffian!"

"B-but, I-I didn't . . ." faltered Bully Bear. "I thought the prizes were here. I-I mean . . ."

"Thought you'd have them for yourself, did you?" thundered Captain Bear. He almost threw Bully Bear across the beach!

"Go away," he roared, "and don't come back, spoiling things for everyone else!"

"See that, Teddy?" grinned Barney. "Good thing Bully believed the note you wrote about the prizes being buried under Captain's sand-castle!" Clever Teddy Bear!

24

The Three Bears

Teddy Bear loves honey! Best of all, he likes it spread on hot toast at breakfast-time. So he's a bit disappointed when he sees Mummy Bear making porridge instead.

"Can't I have honey?" he asks,

"Porridge is good for you on cold mornings like this, Teddy," smiles Mummy. "Come and stir the oats with a little milk in my mixing bowl."

Mixing and stirring is usually one of Teddy's favourite jobs – but Daddy Bear notices that he doesn't look too happy about it, today . . .

"Don't worry about eating up your porridge," he smiles, sitting down in his big chair. "Someone might come along and start eating it for you."

Teddy stops stirring at once.

"Someone eating my porridge?" he cries. "I don't believe it!"

"I expect that's what the other three bears thought," says Mummy, pouring the rest of the milk into a saucepan.

"What other bears?" asks Teddy. He forgets about not having honey for breakfast. "Tell me, Mummy!"

"Well," says Mummy, "there was a Daddy Bear, a Mummy Bear and a Baby Bear. They lived in a cottage at the edge of a wood."

"Just like us!" Teddy says.

"Yes, that's right," Mummy nods, stirring busily.

"Well, this Mummy Bear had just made the porridge, but it was too hot. So, they went for a walk in the woods whilst it cooled down. And along came a little girl with such lovely, long, golden curls that she was called Goldilocks. She saw the three bears' cottage, and went inside."

"And did she eat the porridge?" asks Teddy.

"Only Baby Bear's! She tried Daddy Bear's porridge, but that was too hot, and she tried Mummy Bear's porridge, but that was too cold."

"Then what happened?" Teddy wants to hear the rest of the story, so Mummy tells him how Goldilocks sat in Daddy Bear's chair, but that was too hard.

"Then she sat in Mummy Bear's chair, but that was too soft."

"Did she sit in Baby Bear's chair?" asks Teddy.

Mummy nods again. "Yes. But she was so heavy after eating the porridge, she broke it in pieces! By the time the three bears came back, Goldilocks had gone upstairs to have a rest."

Teddy's Mummy has left the porridge on top of the stove to keep it hot. Now, when she pours it into the breakfast dishes, it is too hot to eat!

"Let's go for a walk," says Daddy. "Just down to the edge of the wood and back."

"Good idea!" agrees Mummy. "It's such a lovely, crisp morning. Put your scarf on, Teddy."

And as they go walking, Mummy finishes the story about Goldilocks and The Three Bears.

"But why did she go into the cottage when nobody was at home?" says Teddy at last.

"I think she smelt the porridge," says Mummy.

"And it was Baby Bear's porridge that she ate," Daddy reminds him.

"But, it's only a story. . ." begins Teddy.

30

Then, he stops. He is sure he has just seen someone going towards the little cottage at the edge of the wood . . . someone with long, golden curls bobbing about in the breeze . . .

"Come on!" he shouts, and begins to run as fast as he can. "Let's go home!"

He has quite decided that he doesn't want Goldilocks eating up **his** porridge, this morning!

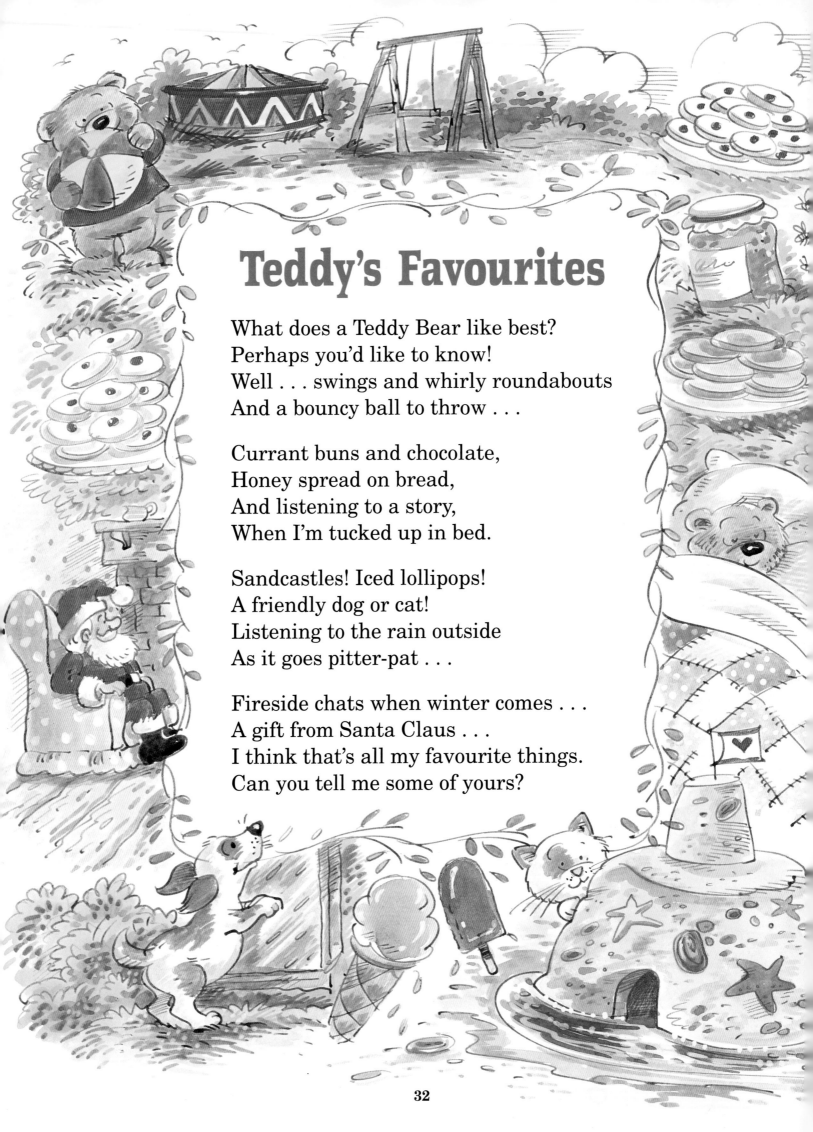

Teddy's Favourites

What does a Teddy Bear like best?
Perhaps you'd like to know!
Well . . . swings and whirly roundabouts
And a bouncy ball to throw . . .

Currant buns and chocolate,
Honey spread on bread,
And listening to a story,
When I'm tucked up in bed.

Sandcastles! Iced lollipops!
A friendly dog or cat!
Listening to the rain outside
As it goes pitter-pat . . .

Fireside chats when winter comes . . .
A gift from Santa Claus . . .
I think that's all my favourite things.
Can you tell me some of yours?

Teddy Goes Flying

One morning, Teddy Bear was looking out of the window for quite a long time.
"What are you looking at, Teddy?" asked Mummy Bear at last.
"I'm watching the birds," Teddy Bear told her. He gave a little sigh. "Oh, Mummy! It must be lovely to fly around wherever you want to go, just like them! Do you think I could learn?"

"Birds have lovely, feathery wings," she said. "So they're the ones who fly! But we can do lots of other things, can't we?" Teddy did not answer. Then he saw something moving along the window sill. It was a ladybird! Teddy loved to see these pretty little creatures. He held out his paw.

Teddy began to say the nursery rhyme which Mummy Bear had taught him. "Ladybird, ladybird . . ." Teddy Bear stopped. Then, he thought hard. Then, he blew very gently on his paw. The ladybird spread her little wings and flew out of the window. Yet, Mummy Bear hadn't said anything at all about beetles being able to fly!

Teddy Bear wandered outside,
where butterflies were flitting among
the flowers! "More things that can fly!"
he thought. Then he heard two bears
calling to each other. "See it fly!"
"Look, up it goes! It's flying!"
It was a beautiful kite sailing up
towards the sky and trailing a bright
paper tail behind it.
"Of course!" cried Teddy. "Kites fly, too!"
He remembered something else.

Kites were like teddy bears. They did not have any wings, either. Just then, an aeroplane streaked across the sky, the sun glinting on its wings – wings which were nothing like the light, feathery wings of the birds. So, how did they fly? After a bit more thinking, Teddy made up his mind to try to fly himself.

But he did not know how to start. He tried jumping, both feet together and flapping his arms about like wings. Then he tried hopping, first on one leg, then on the other. It was quite fun! But Teddy had to stop because he felt so hot and out of breath.

"Maybe," he thought, "if I was up a bit higher, then jumped and flapped my arms, I might fly!" So off he went to Honeypot Hill, climbing up and up to the top. It seemed much higher than it did from his bedroom window. But nothing was going to stop Teddy, now! He shut his eyes tight, made a little run, held his breath – and jumped!

He forgot all about flapping his arms. SPLAT! Teddy landed – splash! – right in the muddy stream at the bottom! "Mummy!" he shouted, feeling all sticky and squelchy and gooey! "Daddy!"

"Teddy!" boomed a voice. "What are you doing down there?" It was Teddy's Uncle Sailor Bill, out flying in the navy helicopter.

Muddy and wet, Teddy Bear was soon hauled up on a rope, higher and higher, towards the helicopter. "I only wanted to fly!" he told his uncle. "Well," laughed Uncle Bill, "you got your wish!"

"Yes," said Teddy, "but the birds, the butterflies, the ladybird and the kite made it look so easy!" He had already decided that flying back to Bear Cottage in a helicopter was exciting enough!

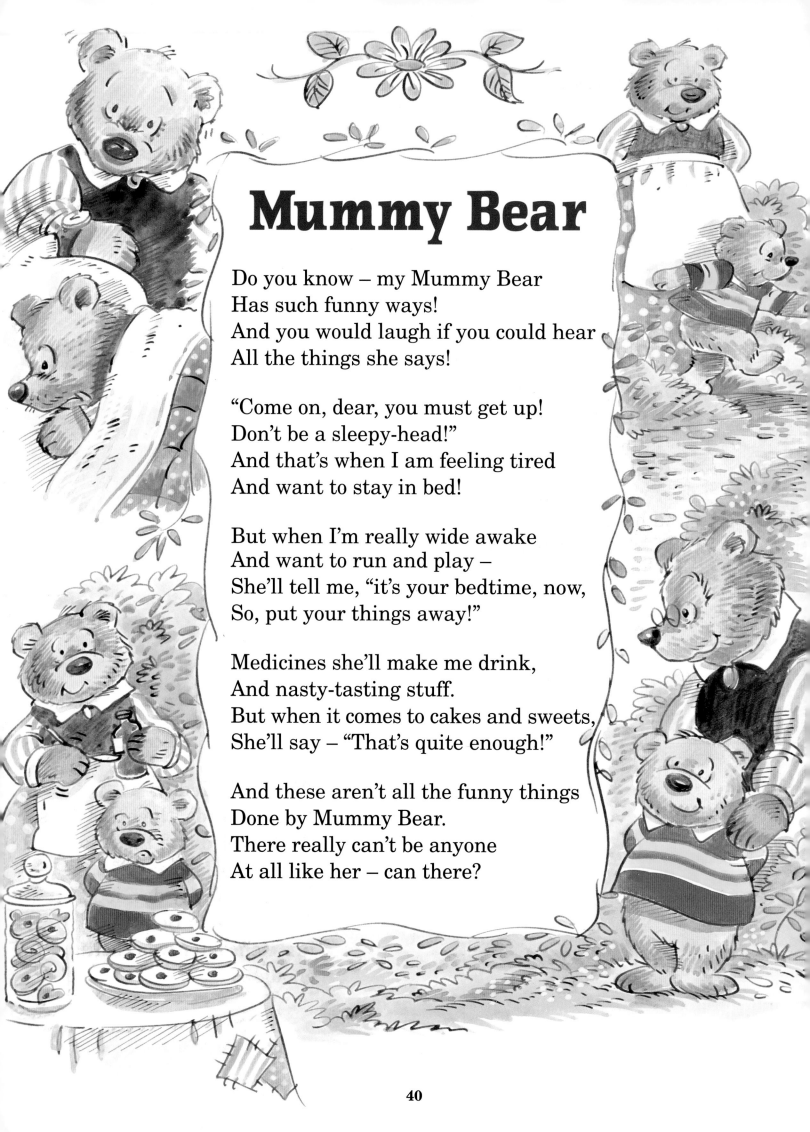

Mummy Bear

Do you know – my Mummy Bear
Has such funny ways!
And you would laugh if you could hear
All the things she says!

"Come on, dear, you must get up!
Don't be a sleepy-head!"
And that's when I am feeling tired
And want to stay in bed!

But when I'm really wide awake
And want to run and play –
She'll tell me, "it's your bedtime, now,
So, put your things away!"

Medicines she'll make me drink,
And nasty-tasting stuff.
But when it comes to cakes and sweets,
She'll say – "That's quite enough!"

And these aren't all the funny things
Done by Mummy Bear.
There really can't be anyone
At all like her – can there?

Uncle Sailor Bill

Teddy is so excited today. His Uncle Sailor Bill has promised to take him and all his friends on a special boat trip to Plumtree Island, with a picnic and a sing-song around a camp-fire.

Only Mummy Bear seems worried. She has seen the big storm clouds gathering in the sky . . . .

Suddenly, down comes the rain.

"Quick!" cries Teddy. "Make for the boat-house!"

Poor Teddy! He and his friends have been looking forward to their special treat for so long – and now it looks as if it is all going to be spoilt.

"My Uncle Sailor Bill has sailed half-way round the world!" Teddy tells everyone. "A thunder storm won't stop him from getting here."

He has hardly finished speaking, when – guess who comes into the boat-house, shaking a shower of raindrops from his hat? That's right! It's Uncle Sailor Bill, smiling all over his face.

"Ahoy there, me hearties!" he calls out in his loud voice. "Just the weather for a shipwreck, eh?"

"A shipwreck?" echoes Teddy.

"That's right," smiles Uncle Sailor Bill. "Come on, shipmates! Let's collect up all the things we can use to keep afloat."

Then, do you know what Uncle Sailor Bill
does next? He turns every chair upside-down!

"This is going to be the best shipwreck, ever,"
he keeps saying. "Teddy, see if you can roll up
that mat, will you?"

"All right, Uncle," says Teddy.

Nobody quite knows what is happening, but
it seems a lot of fun.

By the time they have finished, the boat-house looks such a mess! As well as the upturned chairs, there are planks of wood and empty chests all over the place, rolled-up mats and piles of old sacks . . .

Mummy Bear holds up her paws in horror – but Teddy and his friends are so busy enjoying themselves, they don't even think about the rain pouring down outside.

"Look lively, shipmates!" booms Uncle Sailor Bill. "Time to get all round the wreck without falling into the sea!"

"That means we must try not to step on the floor!" Teddy shouts out. "We don't want to get caught by the pirate king!"

"A pirate king?" Uncle Sailor Bill laughs. "First time I've ever been called that, Teddy!"

When they've all gone round the shipwreck at least twice, Uncle Sailor Bill calls out: "Time for ship's rations!" and throws back the lid of a great, big picnic hamper packed with all sorts of good things to eat and drink.

Then Uncle Sailor Bill takes out his concertina, and everyone is soon joining in with all the jolly songs that they know.

Suddenly, one of the little bears gives a cry.

"Look, everyone! It's stopped raining!"

"So it's a voyage to Plumtree Island, after all," says Uncle Sailor Bill. "Get the boat-house ship-shape, then we set sail."

The boat ride to Plumtree Island is lovely – but because of the rain, Uncle Sailor Bill says it's too wet to land.

"Sorry, shipmates," he says. "Maybe, next time, eh? When it's fair weather for sailing."

Teddy smiles round at his friends. Each of them can't help hoping for another shipwreck the next time they meet his Uncle Sailor Bill!

Teddy Bear's Partytime

Teddy Bear is getting everything ready to invite his friends to a party! Can you help, by telling him who gets which party package?

Teena Bear's favourite colour is red. She's hoping for a matching party hat and balloon.

Billy Bear loves waving flags! He does not like wearing a hat!

Posy wants a striped party hat, striped candy cane and a striped balloon.

Bella likes stripes best! She's getting a red striped hat and red striped candy canes.

Barney Bear wants a plain hat and flag but no balloon.

Bobby Bear would like a striped balloon and a plain hat.

1

2

3

4

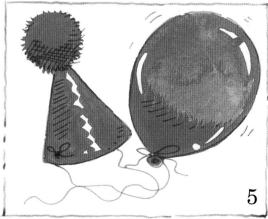

5

6

Answer:- Teena - 5, Bella - 6, Billy - 1, Barney - 2, Posey - 4, Bobby - 3

Round and Round
the Garden

Round and round the garden,
Like a teddy bear,
One step, Two steps,
Tickle you under there.

Round and round the haystack,
Went the little mouse.
One step, Two steps,
In his little house.

Teddy Bear's Surprise

Teddy Bear was feeling so bored! Mummy Bear was busy in the kitchen, Daddy had gone to the market, and there did not seem much to do.

"I've done all my jigsaws!" he told Mummy Bear. "And I've tidied the toy cupboard!"

"What about digging in the garden?" smiled Mummy. "Plant some vegetables if you like."

"All right," sighed Teddy. He was not really in the mood for gardening.

"I'll go and ask Barney Bear to help."

"Cheer up, Teddy!" Mummy smiled again. "You might have a nice surprise before long!" But Teddy did not think so. And when he found Barney Bear was not at home, he was not at all pleased.

Of course, Teddy should have gone straight back home. Instead, he just marched away.

He didn't look where he was going and
didn't care that he might get lost! Soon,
instead of being bored and angry,
Teddy Bear felt so sad and lonely that
he might have begun to cry – except,
just at that very moment, he heard
somebody laughing . . .

"That's right, ship-mates!" boomed a loud, jolly voice Teddy knew well. "Just enjoy yourselves!" "Uncle Sailor Bill!" cried Teddy, running as fast as he could to where all the laughing and chatter was coming from. "Uncle Sailor Bill, it's me! Teddy Bear!" "Well, scupper me scallywags!" laughed Uncle Bill.
"Come and meet my friends, Teddy!"

Well, there was Posy and Primrose, the twins, Billy Bear and Bobby Bear, Susie, Bella, Tom and Timmy, and lots more bears, all talking and laughing and feeling very excited. "We're going on a treasure hunt!" cried Posy. "There's a picnic first!" said Primrose. "It's a lovely place where we're going, Teddy."

"Do you think Mummy will mind if I come?" Teddy asked. "I think she'll find out soon enough!" laughed Uncle Sailor Bill. Teddy was so pleased! All along the way, Bobby told him about the games of hide-and-seek they would have. "Wait until you see all the hidey-holes, Teddy!" he said. "And the squirrels, and the trees we can climb!"

"And the rounders field!" added Bella. Teddy began to wonder where this exciting place could possibly be. And every time he tried asking about it, Uncle Sailor Bill was busy, either lifting little bears over stiles or making sure nobody was getting left behind. "You'll find out soon enough, Teddy!" was all he would say!

Once or twice, Teddy thought he knew where he was. The clock tower through the trees looked rather like the one in the market near his home, and there was a water fountain he thought he had seen before . . .

"Nearly there, Teddy!" laughed Bobby Bear! "Race you through the trees!" "Don't want to miss the picnic!" cried Billy. Still laughing, they ran through a tunnel of cool, leafy trees with Teddy Bear chasing after them.

This was better than staying at home with nothing to do, he thought! And he made up his mind to ask Uncle Sailor Bill why they couldn't have fun like this where he lived. Teddy chased Billy and Bobby out into the sunshine – and do you know where he found himself?

56

Across the path from his own front garden!
"You said we were going to this lovely place,"
he told Posy, "with hidey-holes and squirrels
and trees to climb and fields to play in . . ."
"That's right, Teddy!" cried Bobby, swinging
from a tree. "Now, we'll have some fun!"
Just then, out came Mummy Bear with lots
of lovely things for the picnic!

"I see you've met your new friends, Teddy!" she
smiled. "Didn't I say you'd be getting a nice
surprise?"
"Yes," said Teddy, "you did." And he looked
around at the duck pond, and the swing
and the wishing well . . . all the places he loved.
"But coming home was the best surprise of all!"

My Teddy Bear

My Teddy Bear
May not have any hair -
But he's always ready to play!
Whatever I do,
Teddy Bear joins in, too.
And we're always together, each day.

My Teddy Bear
Comes with me, everywhere!
At home, in the park or the car.
All my secrets he hears,
But I have no fears
He'll tell anyone what they are!

When we sit down to eat,
Teddy's there, on his seat,
With the things that he likes on my plate.
And his milk in my cup, -
I'll drink it all up!
We're agreed on the things that we hate.

Soon, it's Good-Night,
And, both curled up tight,
We go to sleep at the day's end -
Until the bright sun
Says morning's begun -
With a new day for me and my friend.

The Doll's House

Teddy Bear always likes calling in to see his friend, the Toymaker. His workshop is such a nice, warm place to be, with lots of interesting things going on.

"Nice to see you, Teddy!" the Toymaker smiled one morning. "Come over to my bench and tell me what you think of this doll's house I'm making for the Children's Hospital."

Teddy, thought how pleased the children would be.

"Isn't it their party tomorrow?" asked Teddy.

"Yes," said the Toymaker.

Next day, Teddy decided to go past the Children's Hospital on his way to the Toymaker's workshop.

Everyone was busy, putting up decorations and setting out the tables ready for the party

"If only the children had something nice to see from their balcony, instead of this ugly, old wall," sighed Matron.

"Even the birds don't stay long because there is nowhere for them to feed!"

Teddy wished he could help.

"Not much fun sitting out on a balcony when there is nothing to see. Never mind!" he told himself. "Just wait until the Toymaker brings the lovely doll's house!" He could hardly wait to see it, himself!

But, as he turned the corner, the Toymaker came hurrying towards him, looking very upset.

"Such a dreadful thing has happened, Teddy!" he cried. "I left my workshop window open last night so that the paint would dry, and the rain came in and made the wood swell. Now the walls don't fit, so I can't put the floors in, either!"

"Oh, dear!" said Teddy. "And you worked so hard!"

Then Teddy had an idea!

"Toymaker," he said, "can you fix some hooks to the bottom of the house, and take out the back wall? Perhaps make the roof a bit thicker, too?"

"Yes," said the Toymaker in surprise, "but . . ."

"Do that, then bring it to the Children's Hospital," said Teddy. "I'll meet you there."

And off Teddy went into the woods with his Daddy. Together, they collected all the nuts and berries and pips they could find. Then Mummy Bear gave them some pieces of stale bread and an old saucer – and off they all went to meet the Toymaker at the Children's Hospital.

It really was a very good idea . . .

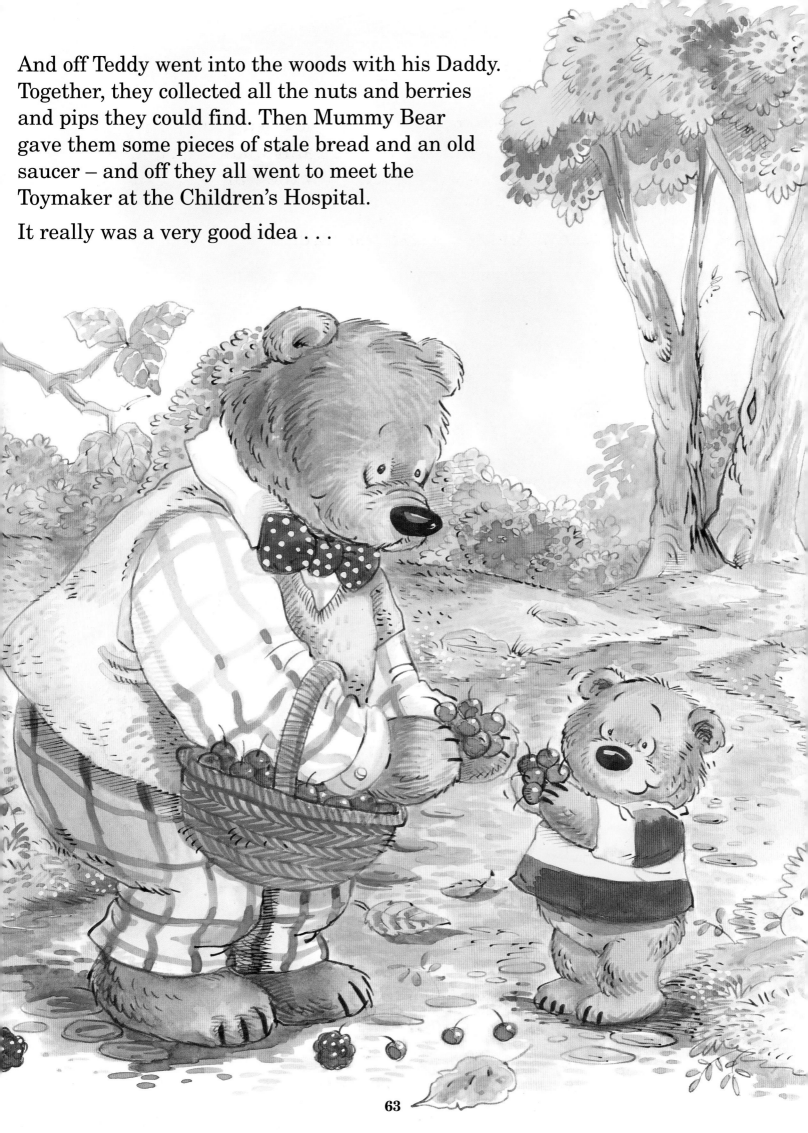

Soon, the Toymaker was fixing the strange-looking house on to the wall . . . And even before Teddy had put out all the berries, the nuts, the pips, the stale bread and a saucer of water, birds began flying in and out of their new home!

"What a sight for the children to see from the balcony!" cried Matron. "Thank you, Toymaker!"

"And thank you, Teddy!" smiled the Toymaker.